# Essential Melodic & Harmonic Patterns

## for

## Group Piano Students

by

### James Lyke

Professor of Music, Emeritus
University of Illinois, Urbana-Champaign

### Geoffrey Haydon

Associate Professor of Music
Georgia State University, Atlanta

Pubished by
STIPES PUBLISHING COMPANY
204 West University Avenue
Champaign, Illinois 61820

GRAPHIC DESIGN AND LAYOUT BY
CP MUSIC ENGRAVING, CHICAGO, ILLINOIS

ISBN 1-58874-187-7

# Preface
## TO THE FOURTH EDITION

Previous versions of *Essential Melodic and Harmonic Patterns for Group Piano Students* were published as *First Year Piano Patterns with Rhythm Background, Vols. I and II* (1973) and *Early Level Piano Patterns with Instrumental Accompaniment, Vols. I and II* (1989). The 1973 edition came with an LP record and the 1989 edition included two cassette tapes. The present edition includes a "play along" CD containing both audio tracks and embedded Standard MIDI Files. The tracks have been digitally recorded by co-author Dr. Geoffrey Haydon.

*Essential Melodic and Harmonic Patterns for Group Piano Students* is designed to assist elementary and intermediate level keyboard students in learning basic melodic and harmonic keyboard patterns. Patterns include major and minor pentachords in all keys, scales built in tetrachords in all keys, major and minor triads in arpeggio form, and various basic chord progressions. New material added to previous editions includes blues scale patterns and the blues chord progression. The ii$^7$-V$^7$-I$^{\Delta 7}$ chord progression, so important to jazz harmony and improvisation, is also introduced to keyboard students. *Essential Melodic and Harmonic Patterns for Group Piano Students* also contains jazz comping (chord accompaniment patterns) techniques and helpful suggestions regarding melodic improvisation. Such activities encourage creativity and ear development.

All melodic and harmonic patterns are completely notated for the student. However, the goal is to have students eventually internalize each pattern. Pattern assignments are left to the discretion of the teacher. The order and amount of patterns assigned to students is therefore flexible enough to efficiently serve their needs within a given curriculum. When patterns are learned and become "second nature," students will become more secure players. They will recognize familiar melodic and harmonic shapes. Such recognition will benefit skills in sight reading, analysis, transposition, and even improvisation.

Teachers should note practice suggestions indicated for each pattern. These ideas are meant to offer alternative ways to practice such as changing articulation, dynamics, rhythm, and/or balance. Students are taught to use creative practice methods that avoid tedious repetition (i.e. rote practicing).

Section One: Melodic Patterns

iv

# TABLE OF
# Contents

## Section One
## Melodic Patterns

## Section Two
## Harmonic Patterns

Essential Melodic & Harmonic Patterns for Group Piano Students

# SECTION ONE
# **Melodic Patterns**

## MAJOR PENTACHORDS

1. <u>Memorize this pattern in all twelve keys</u>. When the pattern is memorized, play with the accompaniment track (with the book closed).

2. There will be a two-bar count off before each pentachord. Prepare for the next major pentachord in the time provided during the rests.

3. **Practice Suggestions**: Play hands alone, play hands together, alternate louds and softs with each new key and alternate touches (*legato* and *staccato*) with each new key.

Section One: Melodic Patterns

 Essential Melodic & Harmonic Patterns for Group Piano Students

Section One: Melodic Patterns

3

## MINOR PENTACHORDS

1. <u>Memorize this pattern in all twelve keys.</u> When the pattern is memorized, play with the accompaniment track (with the book closed).

2. There will be a two-bar count off before each pentachord. Prepare for the next minor pentachord in the time provided by the rests.

3. **Practice Suggestions**: Follow the suggestions listed on page 1. Add the following articulation: two-note slurs using quarter notes ( 𝅘𝅥 𝅘𝅥 𝅘𝅥 𝅘𝅥 | 𝅘𝅥 𝅘𝅥 𝅘𝅥 𝅘𝅥 ).

 Essential Melodic & Harmonic Patterns for Group Piano Students

Section One: Melodic Patterns

6

Essential Melodic & Harmonic Patterns for Group Piano Students

# TETRACHORD SCALES IN C AND SHARP KEYS

1. <u>Memorize this pattern in the eight keys shown</u>. When the pattern is memorized, play with the accompaniment track (with the book closed).

2. There will be a two-bar count off before each scale. Prepare for the new scale in the time provided by the rests.

3. **Practice Suggestions**: Shape each scale by making a crescendo to the top and a diminuendo to the bottom. More advanced students may play one-handed scales using traditional scale fingering. When this is accomplished, play each scale hands together using traditional scale fingering.

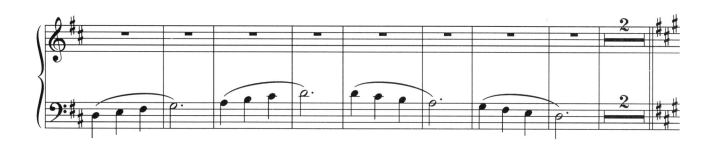

Section One: Melodic Patterns

8

 Essential Melodic & Harmonic Patterns for Group Piano Students

# TETRACHORD SCALES IN FLAT KEYS AND C

1. <u>Memorize this pattern in the eight keys shown</u>. When the pattern is memorized, play with the accompaniment track (with the book closed).

2. There will be a two-bar count off before each scale. Prepare for the new scale in the time provided by the rests.

3. **Practice Suggestions**: Follow the same suggestions listed for Tetrachord Scales in C and Sharp Keys on page 7.

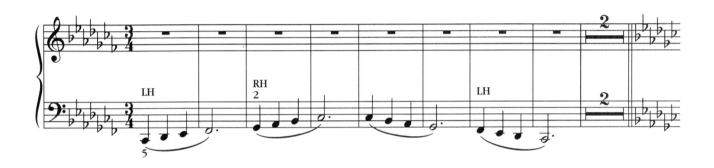

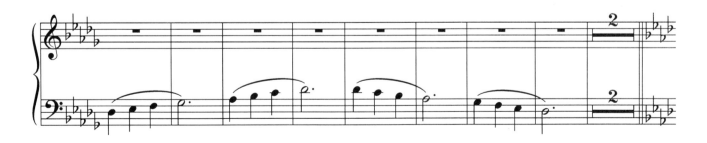

Section One: Melodic Patterns

10

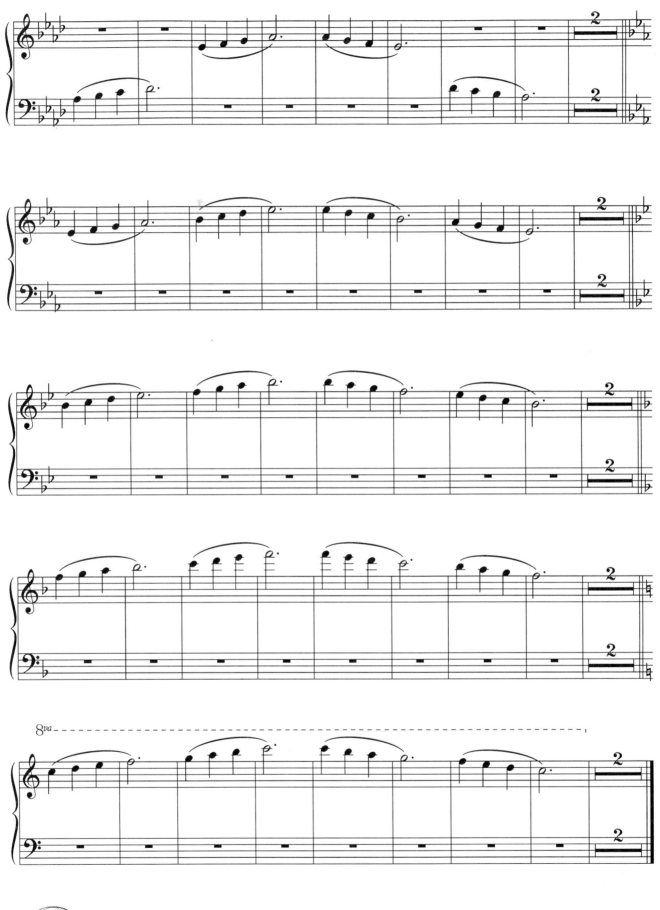

 Essential Melodic & Harmonic Patterns for Group Piano Students

# MAJOR TRIAD ARPEGGIOS

1. <u>Memorize this pattern in all twelve keys.</u> When the pattern is memorized, play with the accompaniment track (with the book closed).

2. There will be a two-bar count off before each arpeggio. Prepare for the next major arpeggio in the time provided by the measure of rest.

3. **Practice Suggestions:** Block each triad as a chord before playing as notated. Alternate *legato* and *staccato* touch with each new key (one key *legato*, the next key *staccato*, etc.). More advanced students may play one-handed arpeggios with traditional fingerings. Following that, play two-handed arpeggios using traditional fingerings.

Section One: Melodic Patterns

12

Essential Melodic & Harmonic Patterns for Group Piano Students

Section One: Melodic Patterns

## MINOR TRIAD ARPEGGIOS

1. <u>Memorize this pattern in all twelve keys</u>. When the pattern is memorized, play with the accompaniment track (with the book closed).

2. There will be a two-bar count off before each arpeggio. Prepare for the next minor arpeggio in the time provided by the measure of rest.

3. **Practice Suggestions**: Follow the same suggestions listed for the Major Triad Arpeggios on page 11.

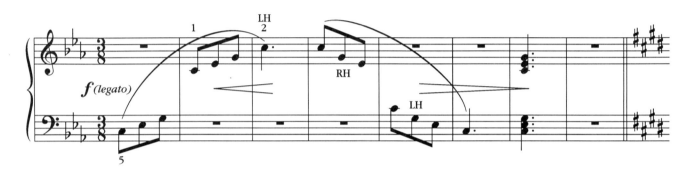

Essential Melodic & Harmonic Patterns for Group Piano Students

Section One: Melodic Patterns

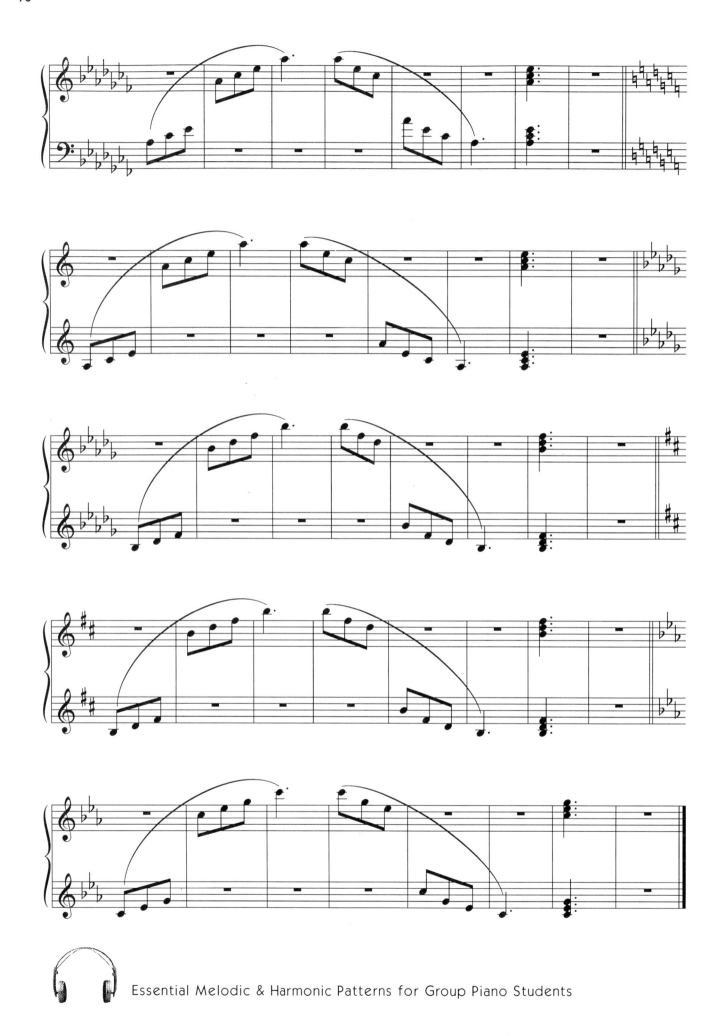

Essential Melodic & Harmonic Patterns for Group Piano Students

# THE BLUES SCALE
### (Keys of D, G, C and F)

1. <u>Memorize these four blues scales in the keys of D, G, C and F</u>. When these scales are memorized, play with the accompaniment track (with the book closed). Learn the structure of the blues scale: root, ♭3rd, 4th, ♯4th (♭5th), 5th and ♭7th.
**Note:** Each four-bar phrase is played three times. This will result in twelve bars in each key.

2. There will be a two-bar count off before each scale. Proceed to each new blues scale with no rhythmic interruption.

3. **Practice Suggestions**: The first time play the scale with the RH. The second time play the scale with the LH. The third time try playing the scale hands together.

Section One: Melodic Patterns

# BLUES BASS LINE
### (Keys of C, F, G and D)

1. Memorize the following bass lines for each twelve bar sequence in C, F, G and D. You will hear dominant seventh harmonies which are shown in the RH part in parentheses. Each twelve bar progression will be repeated once and corresponds to separate tracks (8, 9, 10 and 11) on the CD.

2. **Practice Suggestions**: Play the LH *legato* and keep the fingering consistent.

## KEY OF C

Essential Melodic & Harmonic Patterns for Group Piano Students

# KEY OF F

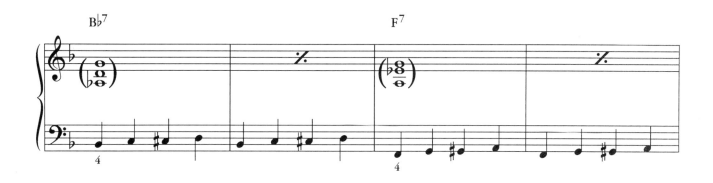

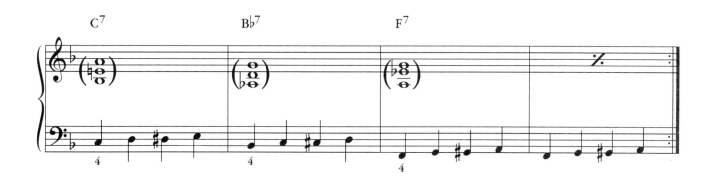

Section One: Melodic Patterns

**KEY OF D**

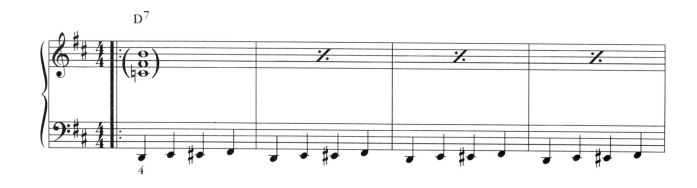

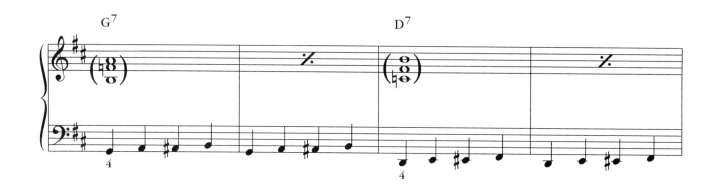

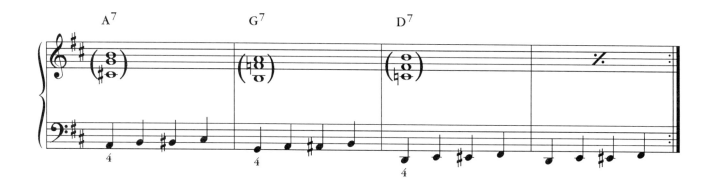

 Essential Melodic & Harmonic Patterns for Group Piano Students

**KEY OF G**

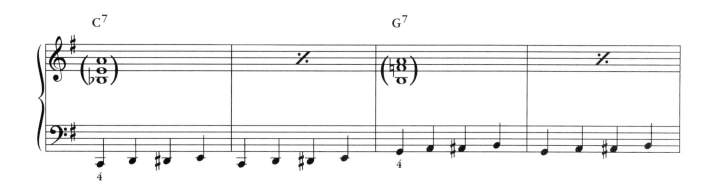

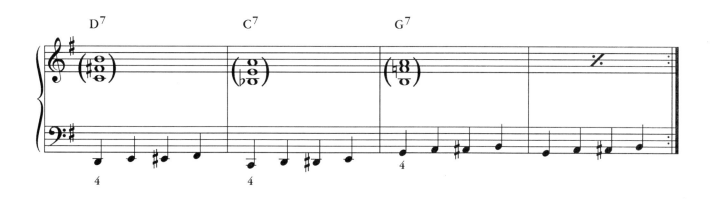

Section One: Melodic Patterns

# SECTION TWO
# Harmonic Patterns

### I–V⁷–I, MAJOR KEYS

1. <u>Memorize this chord progression in all twelve keys</u>. When the progression is memorized, play with the accompaniment track (with the book closed).

2. There will be a two-bar count off before each progression. Prepare for the next progression during the half rest.

3. **Practice Suggestions**: Play one-handed patterns followed by I–V$_5^6$–I in each key (RH, LH and HT). Alternate bass notes for the I–V⁷–I progression as shown in the example for C major below.

Essential Melodic & Harmonic Patterns for Group Piano Students

Section Two: Harmonic Patterns

24

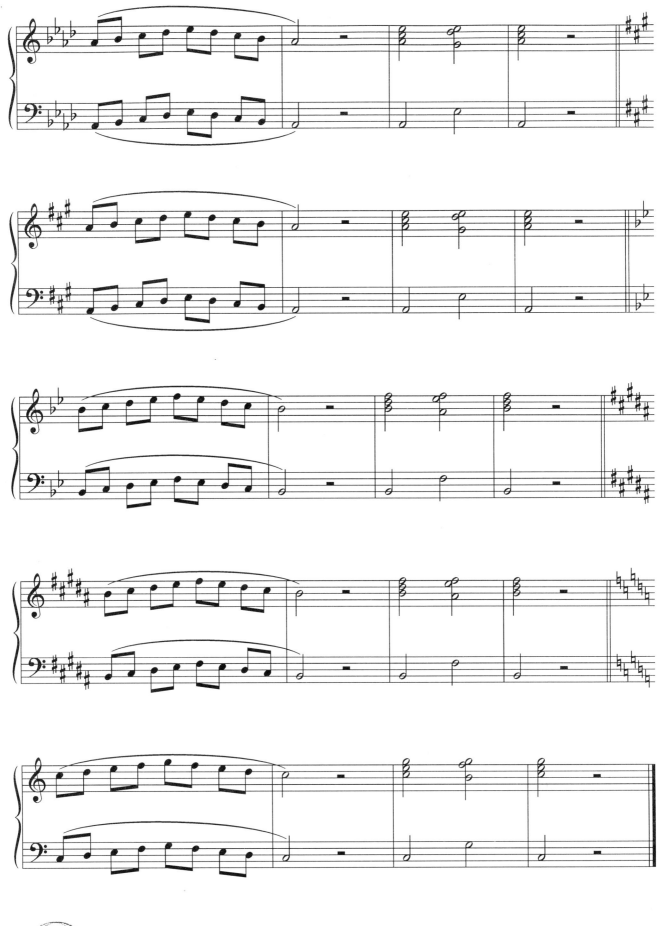

 Essential Melodic & Harmonic Patterns for Group Piano Students

# i–V⁷–i, MINOR KEYS

1. <u>Memorize this chord progression in all twelve keys</u>. When the progression is memorized, play with the accompaniment track (with the book closed).

2. There will be a two-bar count off before each progression. Prepare for the next progression during the half rest.

3. **Practice Suggestions**: Follow the suggestions given for I–V⁷–I, Major Keys on page 22. Apply these to the i–V⁷–i progession in minor keys.

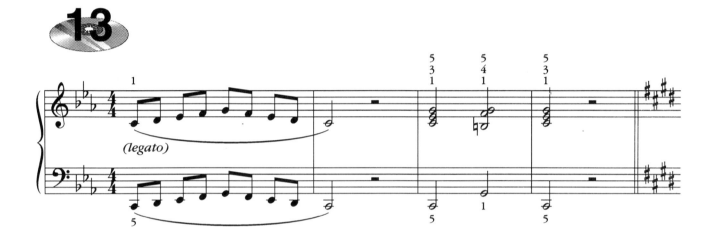

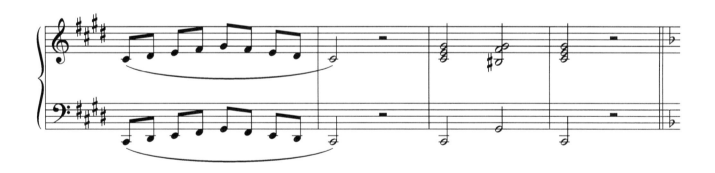

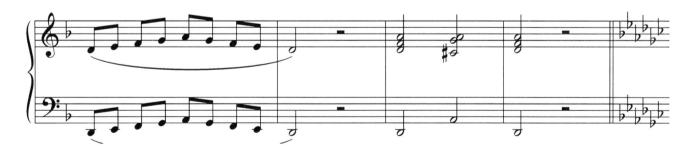

Section Two: Harmonic Patterns

26

Section Two: Harmonic Patterns

# I–IV–I⁶₄–V⁷–I, MAJOR KEYS

1. <u>Memorize this chord progression in all twelve keys</u>. When the progression is memorized, play with the accompaniment track (with the book closed).

2. There will be a two-bar count off before each progression. Prepare for the next progression during the half and whole rests.

3. **Practice Suggestions**: Play one-handed progressions prior to playing hands together. See the examples shown below for C major. Note the alternate bass pattern. This should also be learned.

Essential Melodic & Harmonic Patterns for Group Piano Students

Section Two: Harmonic Patterns

Essential Melodic & Harmonic Patterns for Group Piano Students

## i–iv–i$_4^6$–V$^7$–i, MINOR KEYS

1. <u>Memorize this chord progression in all twelve keys</u>. When the progression is memorized, play with the accompaniment track (with the book closed).

2. There will be a two-bar count off before each progression. Prepare for the new progression during the half and whole rests.

3. **Practice Suggestions**: Follow the same suggestions listed for I–IV–I$_4^6$–V$^7$–I, Major Keys, on page 28. Play one-handed progressions (i–iv–i$_4^6$–V$^7$–i) before playing as shown below. Also, use the alternate bass pattern shown on page 28.

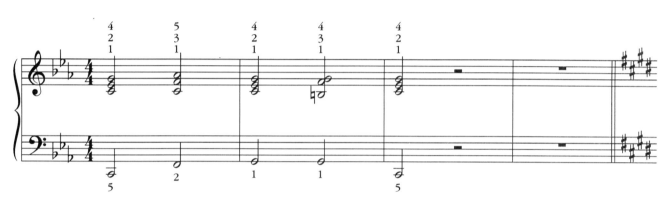

Section Two: Harmonic Patterns

32

Essential Melodic & Harmonic Patterns for Group Piano Students

Section Two: Harmonic Patterns

# CHORD QUALITY EXERCISE
## (Maj–Aug–Maj–Min–Dim)

1. <u>Memorize this pattern in all twelve keys.</u> When the pattern is memorized, play with the accompaniment track (with the book closed).

2. There will be a two-bar count off before each pattern. Prepare for each new pattern during the quarter rest in the 5th bar.

3. **Practice Suggestions**: Keep the fingering the same for each triad (RH: 1–3–5, LH: 5–3–1). Make a *crescendo* and *diminuendo* within each sequence. Gradually increase the speed. Fill in the blanks above each chord as shown in the first pattern.

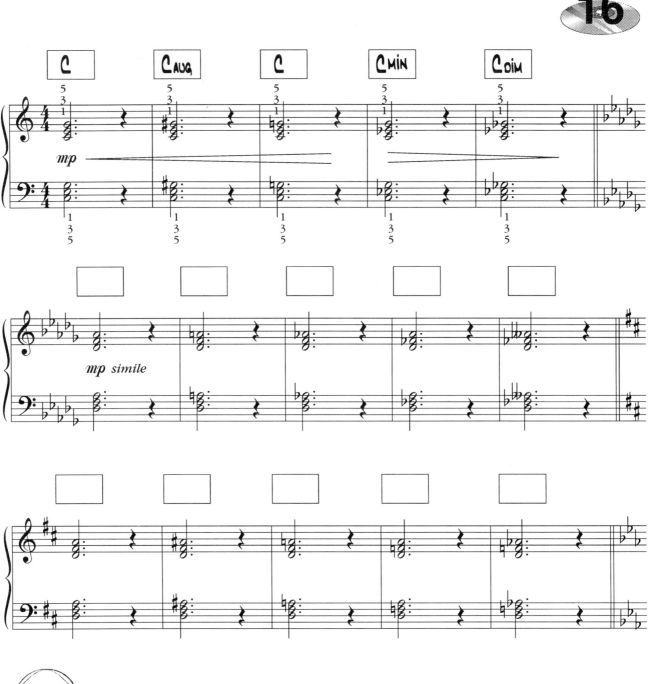

 Essential Melodic & Harmonic Patterns for Group Piano Students

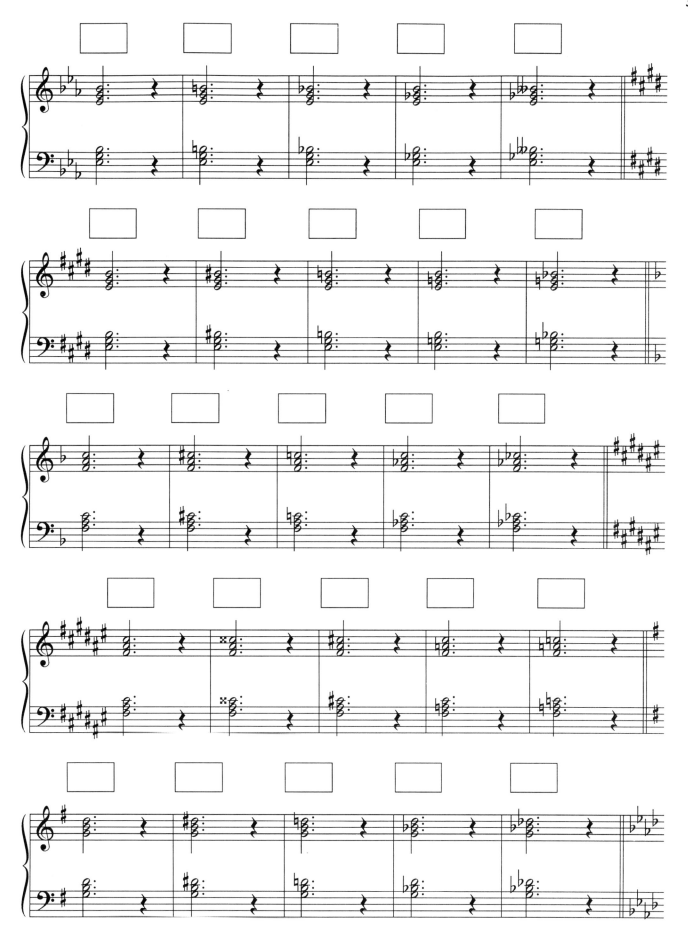

Section Two: Harmonic Patterns

36

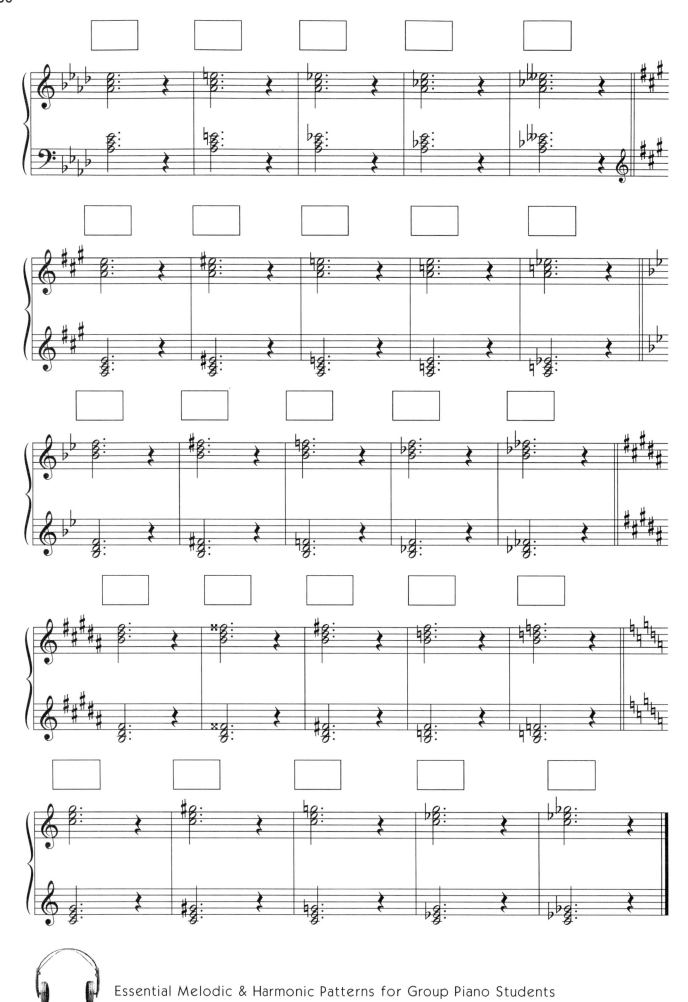

Essential Melodic & Harmonic Patterns for Group Piano Students

# SECONDARY CHORDS

1. <u>Memorize this progression in all twelve keys.</u> When the progression is memorized, play with the accompaniment track (with the book closed).

2. There will be a two-bar count off before each progression. Prepare for the next progression during the whole rest at the end of the sequence.

3. **Practice Suggestions**: Learn the fingering for each hand carefully. Play the LH alone in all keys. Then play the RH alone in all keys. In the RH notice that only one note changes from chord to chord when playing I–vi–IV–ii. When the progression has been memorized, alternate the bass note and RH chords using this pattern: until the final chord (tonic) is reached. Fill in the blanks with the proper chord symbols as shown in the C major progression

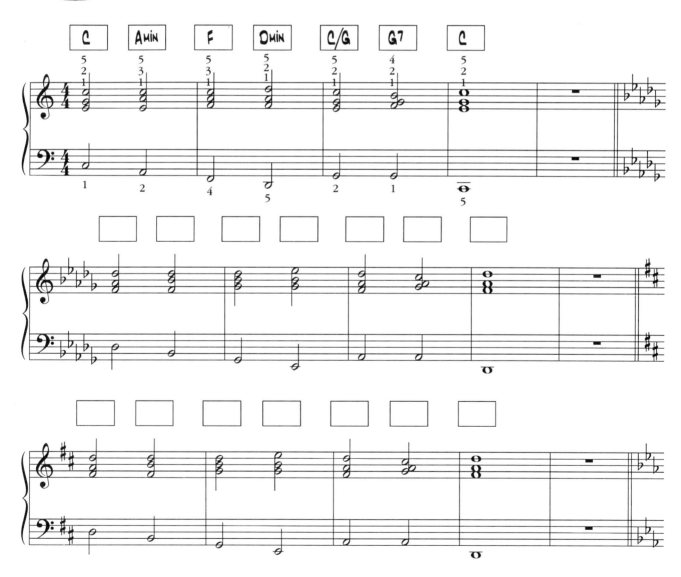

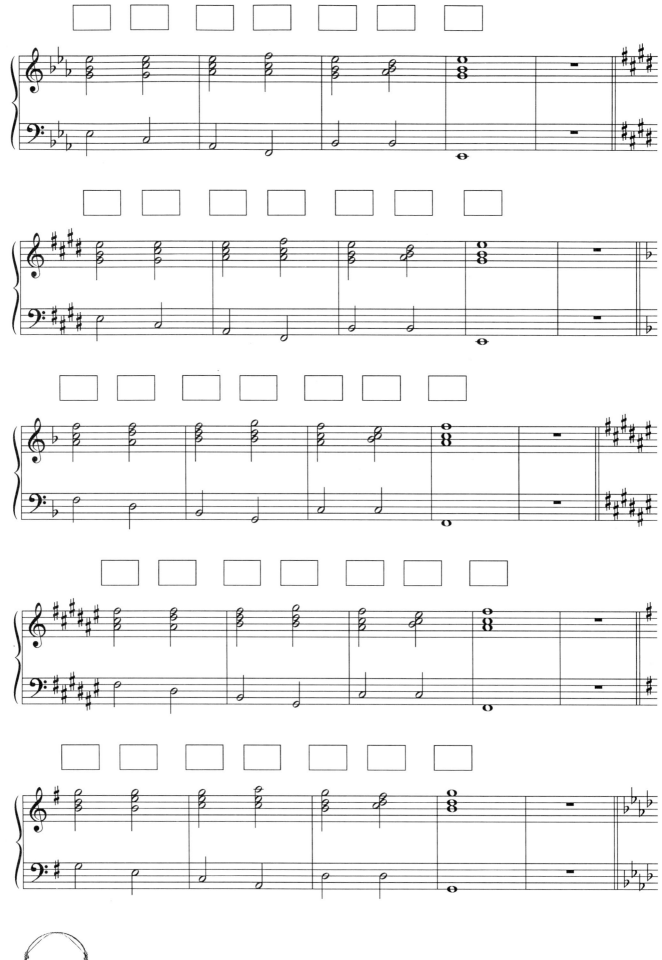

 Essential Melodic & Harmonic Patterns for Group Piano Students

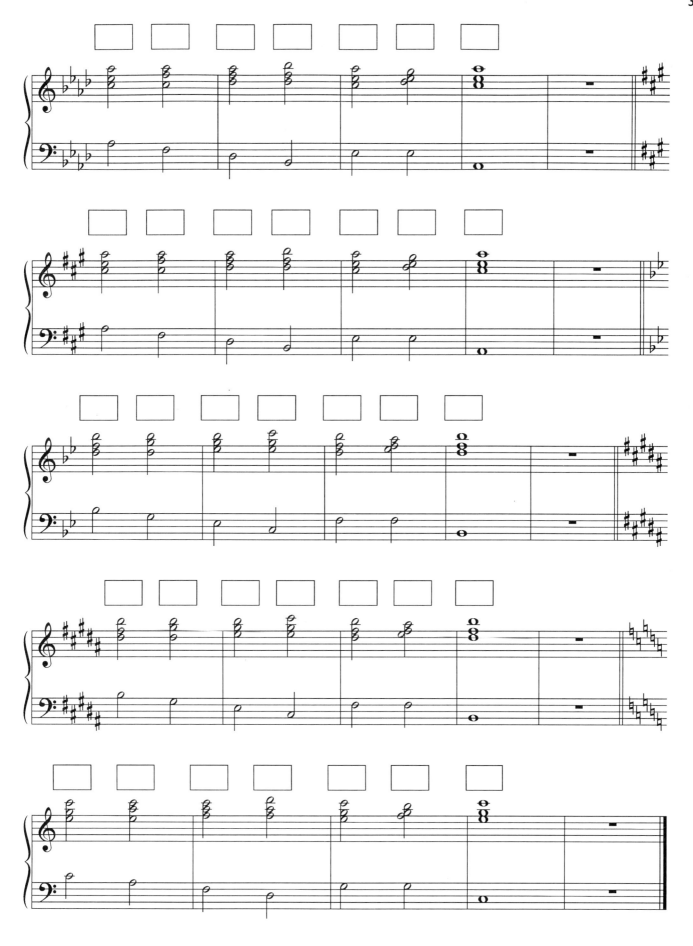

Section Two: Harmonic Patterns

40

# TWELVE BAR BLUES PROGRESSION
## (Key of D)

1. <u>Memorize the twelve bar blues progression in the key of D.</u> When the progression is memorized, play with the accompaniment track (with the book closed).

2. There will be a two-bar count off before the progression begins.

3. **Practice Suggestions:** First play whole note chords in the RH. Then add the already familiar blues bass line. When both hands can operate comfortably, create interesting RH rhythms ("comp" the RH) by playing chords in a more syncopated manner. Below is a good example of "comping" the RH chords.

 Essential Melodic & Harmonic Patterns for Group Piano Students

# TWELVE BAR BLUES PROGRESSION
### (Key of G)

1. <u>Memorize the twelve bar blues progression in the key of G</u>. When the progression is memorized, play with the accompaniment track (with the book closed).

2. There will be a two-bar count off before the progression begins.

3. **Practice Suggestions**: First play whole note chords in the RH. Then add the already familiar blues bass line. When both hands can operate comfortably, create interesting RH rhythms ("comp" the RH) by playing chords in a more syncopated manner. Review the "comping" example on page 40.

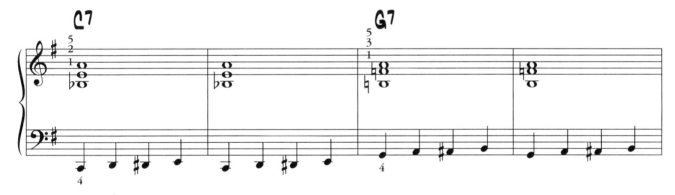

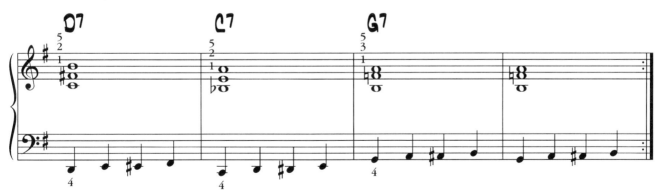

Section Two: Harmonic Patterns

# TWELVE BAR BLUES PROGRESSION
## (Key of F)

1. Memorize the twelve bar blues progression in the key of F. When the progression is memorized, play with the accompaniment track (with the book closed).

2. There will be a two-bar count off before the progression begins.

3. **Practice Suggestions**: First play whole note chords in the RH. Then add the already familiar blues bass line. When both hands can operate comfortably, create interesting RH rhythms ("comp" the RH) by playing chords in a more syncopated manner. Review the "comping" example on page 40.

 Essential Melodic & Harmonic Patterns for Group Piano Students

# TWELVE BAR BLUES PROGRESSION
## (Key of C)

1. <u>Memorize the twelve bar blues progression in the key of C</u>. When the progression is memorized, play with the accompaniment track (with the book closed).

2. There will be a two-bar count off before the progression begins.

3. **Practice Suggestions**: First play whole note chords in the RH. Then add the already familiar blues bass line. When both hands can operate comfortably, create interesting RH rhythms ("comp" the RH) by playing chords in a more syncopated manner. Review the "comping" example on page 40.

Section Two: Harmonic Patterns

# BLUES IMPROVISATION

After mastering the blues progression in the keys of D, G, C and F, you are now ready to explore the art of improvisation using the blues scales covered earlier in the book on page 17. Select a partner and have that person play the blues bass line and "comp" the RH chords. You can improvise above the chords (or at another keyboard) using various notes of the blues scale. The goal is for the improviser to create interesting ideas based on definite rhythmic motives.

It is best to begin working with three adjacent notes selected from the blues scale rather than using all six notes. Study the Blues in C example below which uses a simple three-note idea to create an interesting improvisation.

Use CD/MIDI tracks 22–25 to practice improvising over the twelve bar blues progression in the keys of D, G, C and F.

 Essential Melodic & Harmonic Patterns for Group Piano Students

# TWELVE BAR BLUES IN D

## D Blues Scale

## D Blues Progression

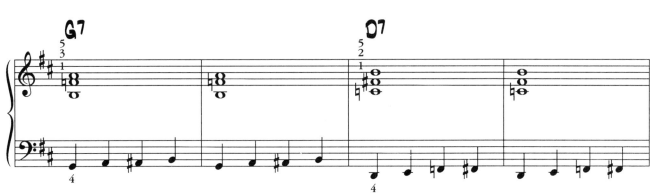

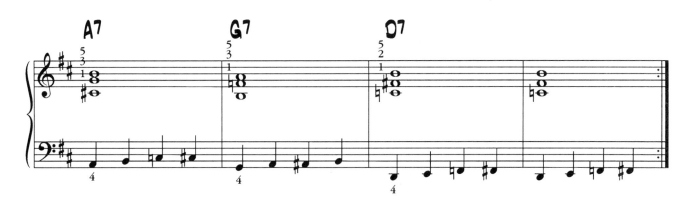

Section Two: Harmonic Patterns

# TWELVE BAR BLUES IN G

## G Blues Scale

## G Blues Progression

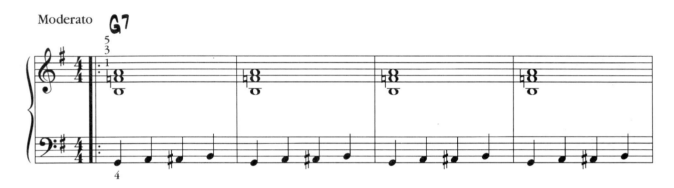

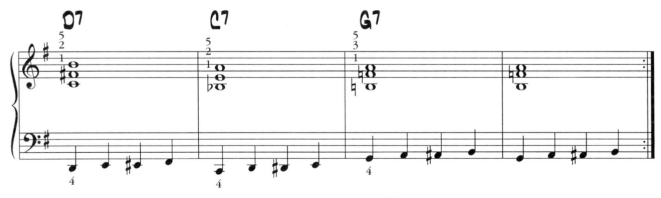

 Essential Melodic & Harmonic Patterns for Group Piano Students

# TWELVE BAR BLUES IN C

## C Blues Scale

## C Blues Progression

Section Two: Harmonic Patterns

# TWELVE BAR BLUES IN F

## F Blues Scale

## F Blues Progression

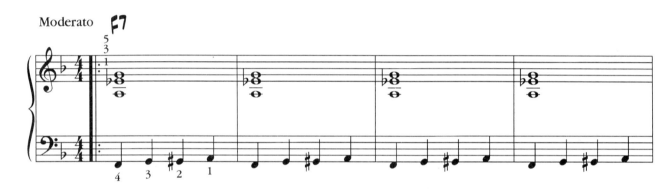

 Essential Melodic & Harmonic Patterns for Group Piano Students

# THE ii⁷–V⁷–I^Δ7 PROGRESSION
## (Keys of C, B♭, A♭, G♭, E, D)

1. <u>Memorize this chord progression in all six keys</u>. When the progression is memorized, play with the accompaniment track (with the book closed). Be satisfied learning a few keys at a time before putting all six together.

2. There will be a two-bar count off before each progression. Prepare for the next progression (be thinking where to place the hands) during the final tied whole notes.

*The ii⁷–V⁷–I^Δ7 progression is common in many jazz standards of composers such as Irving Berlin, Jerome Kern, George Gershwin, Richard Rodgers and Cole Porter. The quality of each of the chords is indicated below.*

$$ii^7 = \textit{minor 7th chord}$$
$$V^7 = \textit{dominant 7th chord}$$
$$I^{\Delta 7} = \textit{major 7th chord}$$

Essential tones in each chord are the root, 3rd and 7th. The following progressions move down by whole steps. Repeat each progression before moving on to the next one.

3. **Practice Suggestions**: Vary the rhythm of the chords. Play in "clave" style as follows:

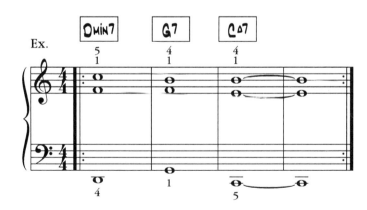

Provide the harmonic background as a partner improvises melodies based on the scale of each chord. For example, the Dm⁷–G⁷–C^Δ7 would use tones of the C major scale. When the pattern of chords has been internalized, change the voicing as shown in the example below.

For the progressions on the following pages, write the proper chord symbols in the box above each chord as shown in the example above.

Section Two: Harmonic Patterns

50

# THE ii⁷–V⁷–I△⁷ PROGRESSION
## (Keys of C, B♭, A♭, G♭, E, D)

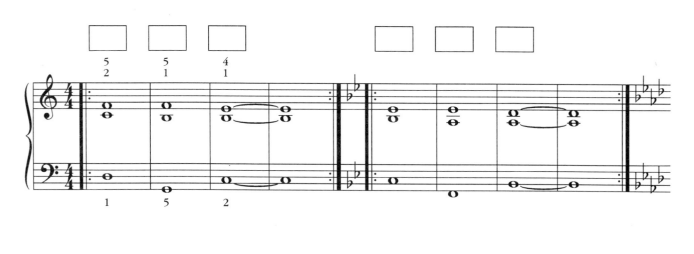

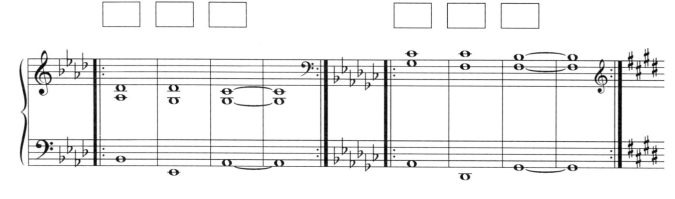

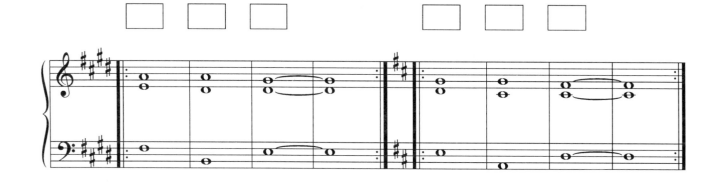

 Essential Melodic & Harmonic Patterns for Group Piano Students

# THE ii⁷–V⁷–I△⁷ PROGRESSION

**(Keys of D♭, B, A, G, F and E♭)**

1. <u>Memorize this chord progression in all six keys.</u> When the progression is memorized, play with the accompaniment track (with the book closed). Be satisfied learning a few keys at a time before putting all six together.

2. There will be a two-bar count off before each progression. Prepare for each new progression (be thinking where to place the hands) during the final tied whole notes.

3. **Practice Suggestions**: Follow the suggestions listed on page 49. Employ the "clave" rhythm. Improvise melodies in the key of each progression. Change the voicing as shown in the example on page 49. Fill in the boxes above each chord with the proper chord symbols (E♭m⁷, A♭⁷, D♭△⁷, etc.).

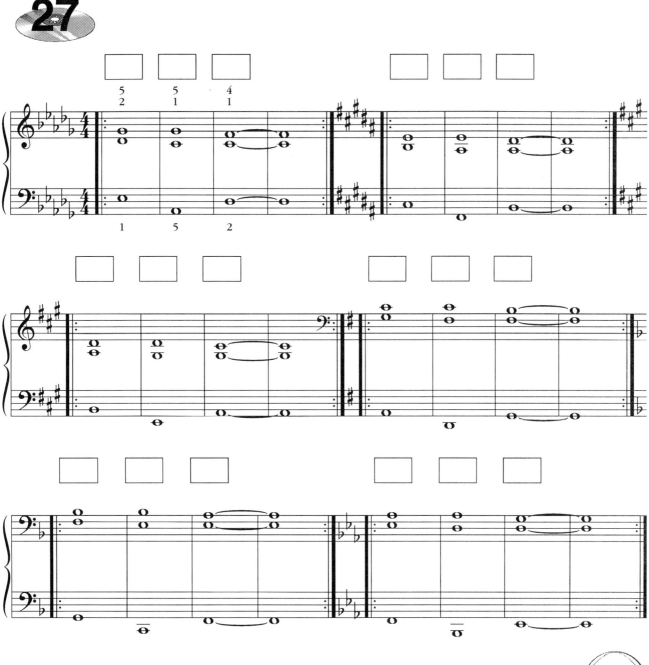

Section Two: Harmonic Patterns

# CD/MIDI
# Accompaniment Tracks

Essential Melodic & Harmonic Patterns for Group Piano Students